To Dad,
and to all the amazing Dads
that build things.
Adam.

For my fabulous Mum, Dad
and sister Jennifer.
Thank you for everything!
Claire.

fourth wall
publishing

First published in Great Britain by Fourth Wall Publishing in 2015.

ISBN: 978-1-910851-04-3

2 Riverview Business Park, Shore Wood Road, Bromborough, Wirral CH62 3RQ.

www.fourthwallpublishing.com

Printed in Turkey.

ROBOT STOP!

Adam Bestwick

Illustrated by Claire Evans

My Dad is an inventor,
And he's building a machine,

It's a kind of housework robot,
To keep my bedroom clean.

When I go up to bed at night,
Dad goes to the cellar,
To work with nuts and bolts
                      and things,
And build this robot fella.

My Mum is so excited,
And says that she can't wait!
A robot chef to wash and clean-
"It's going to be great!"

The next day as the sun comes up,
I'm woken by a

VROOOM!

And something strange and silver,
Is tidying my room!

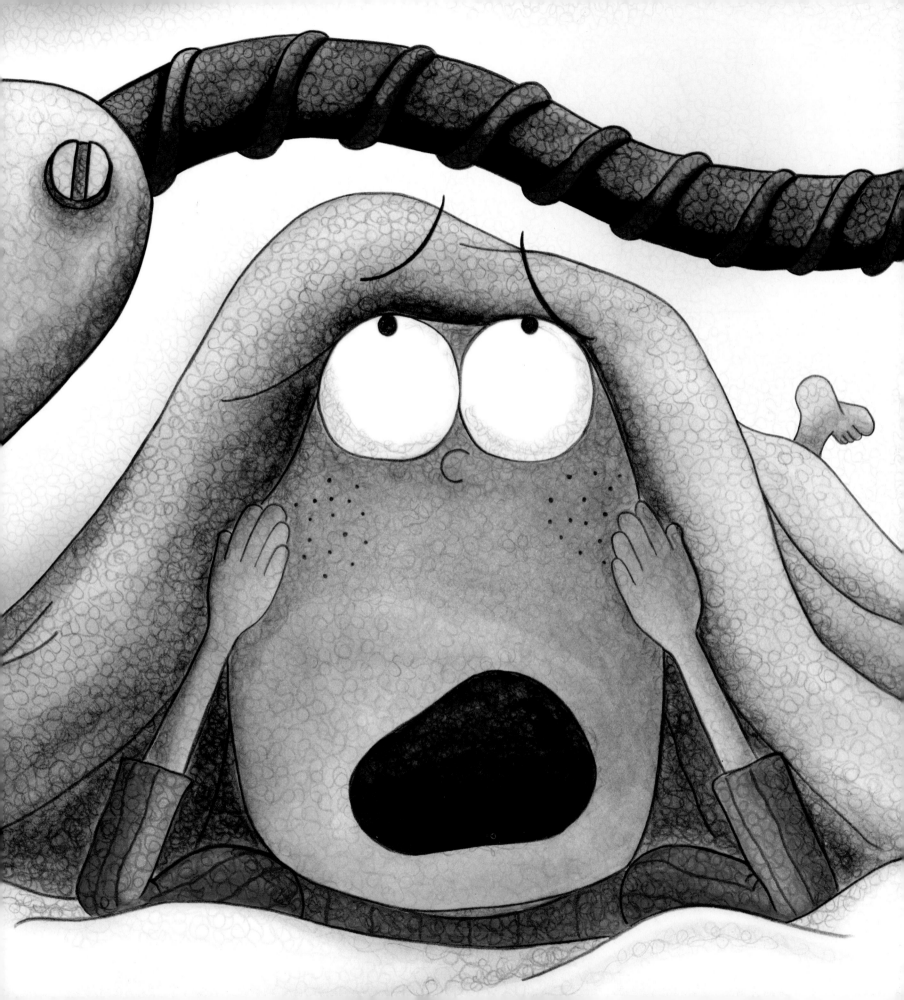

I rub my eyes and can't believe,
It's picking up my blocks!
And toys I'd left upon the floor...

...Even
smelly socks!

When my room is finished,
And looking rather neat,
My Dad says "Come here Robbie
There's someone you should meet!"

"Robbie - meet our robot,
Built in my workshop,
It cooks, it cleans
And sweeps the floor,
'Til I shout ROBOT STOP!"

Robot
Instruction
manual!

So I got dressed and followed it,
To see what it could do,
It washed up all the saucepans,
And made them look brand new!

Dad's robot cleaned the entire house,
From the bottom to the top!
And when the jobs had all been done,
Dad shouted...

"ROBOT STOP!"

The robot stopped on Dad's command,
And it parked-up by the stairs,
"I really love our metal friend
He's the answer to our prayers!"

That night in bed an idea came,
It sounded really cool,
I'll dress the robot up like me,
And send him off to school!

So late that night when it got dark,
With Mum and Dad in bed,

I dressed the robot in my clothes,
And put my cap upon his head.

Next day my plan was working,
And Mum just didn't see!
As we left to walk to school,
She waved to 'robot me!'

"Now off you go nice robot,
And please work hard at school..."

"Real Robbie is off
skateboarding,
This plan is really cool!"

The robot zoomed off on his way,
But stomped right through a puddle,

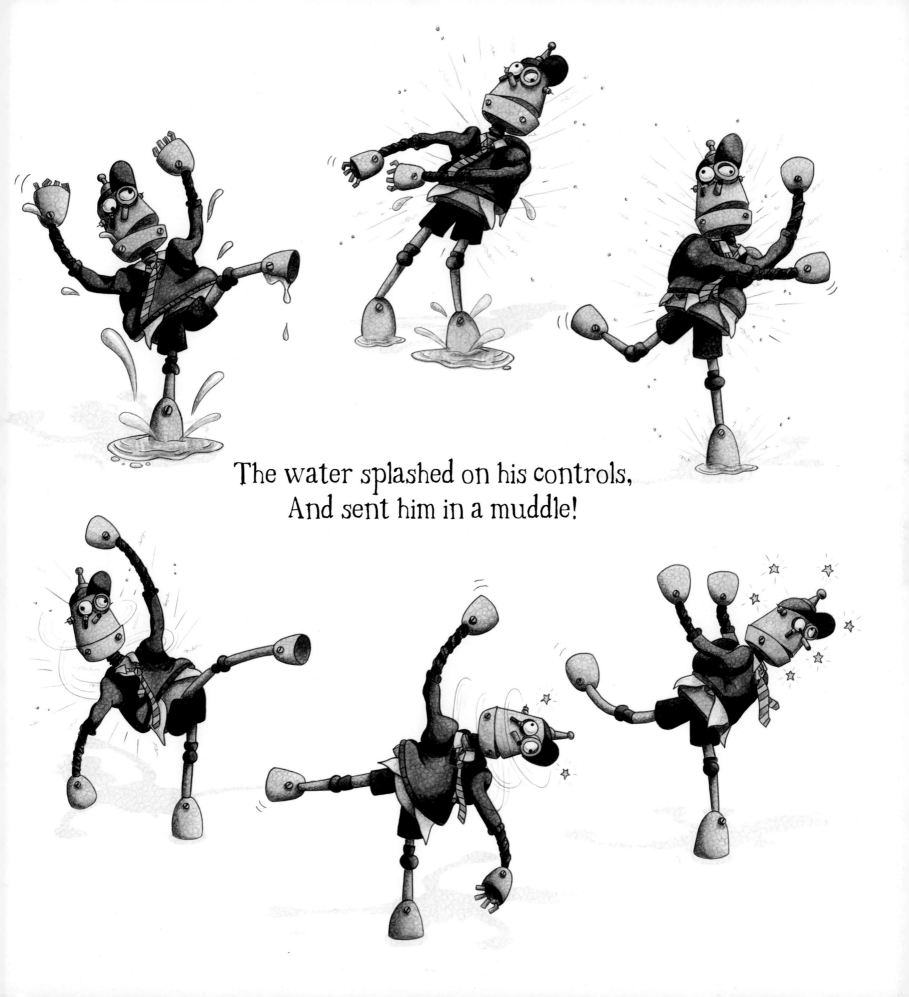

The water splashed on his controls,
And sent him in a muddle!

As 'robot Robbie' reached the school,
All dizzy, seeing stars...
He smashed straight through the playground fence,
And squashed the teachers' cars!

The children shouted

"ROBBIE, NO!"

They didn't realise...
This techno Robbie look-alike
Was robot in disguise!

The robot smashed the classroom wall,
And started munching books,
It sucked up chairs, and desks and pens,
...Even the coat hooks!

ABCDEFGHIJKLMNOPQRSTUVWXYZ

The Headmaster
telephoned my Dad,
"Come quickly, we're in trouble..!
Your son's gone mad –
he's lost control,
He'll turn the school to rubble!"

Then, in his car and on his way,
Dad spots me having fun,

"You'd best jump in you naughty boy,
There's explaining to be done!"

So I sit and tell my Dad the truth,
About this silly plan,
Of sending robot off to school,
And how it all began.

When we arrive outside the school,
It's quite an awful sight,

SCHOOL ENTRANCE

'Our robot's made a frightful mess,
It's time to put things right!"

So with a deep breath, my Dad and I,
Give an ENORMOUS shout...

"ROBOT STOP

...And all-at-once
his big round eyes go out.

PHEW!

So what happened to our robot?
Well, it's on display at home...

He's pride of place outside our door...
Our techno garden gnome!